Coloring the Community

 SRA

Columbus, OH

SRAonline.com

 SRA

Send all inquiries to this address:
SRA/McGraw-Hill
4400 Easton Commons
Columbus, OH 43219

ISBN: 978-0-07-608857-7
MHID: 0-07-608857-X

1 2 3 4 5 6 7 8 9 NOR 13 12 11 10 09 08 07

Ms. Sanchez had just finished showing the class a slide show of famous murals, and the rich paintings of Diego Rivera were fresh in their minds.

"So you see," she said, "a mural is a painting on a wall, but it is much more than that because it has the power to bring people together and make them proud."

"That's so incredible," said Renata, who loved to draw and paint. "Ms. Sanchez, could we create a mural?"

An excited buzz went through the room.

Ms. Sanchez beamed as she said, "That's what I hoped you would ask, but a mural takes a lot of planning. We'll begin by writing to Mayor Peña."

That same day, the class composed a letter.

Dear Mayor Peña:

Our class has been learning about murals. Besides being beautiful and exciting, these artworks also can represent the heritage of a community. They can show how the community began and all the people who make it work.

Our town is a great place to live. We want to paint a mural about our community. We think our community deserves a mural. Don't you? Please write and let us know where we can put our mural.

Sincerely,
Ms. Sanchez's Sixth-Grade Class
Painted Sands Elementary School

In a few days, an official-looking envelope arrived.

Dear students:

You do have an excellent idea! Our town is indeed
a wonderful place to live, and this is just the kind
of project that can help citizens feel pride in their
community.

However, before we can undertake a project like this,
many questions must be answered: What will the mural
contain, and where will it be? Who will be in charge?
How will funds for the mural be obtained? And finally,
when will the mural be painted?

I look forward to reading your plan.

Sincerely,

Mayor Maria Peña

The students had many different ideas for the mural, and everyone began talking at once.

"Class, please!" cried Ms. Sanchez. "You must take turns so all the good ideas will be heard."

"Native Americans lived here first," said Renata, "and we should show their pueblos and crops."

"What about the pioneers?" asked Van. "They sacrificed a lot to come here, and they built this town."

"I think we should put desert plants and animals in the mural," said Tanya. "After all, we live in the desert, and these living things are our neighbors too." Soon there was a very long list on the paper.

"I think we need one big idea to pull our mural together," said Ms. Sanchez. "It should be an idea that includes everything we've been discussing."

The students agreed that their community was diverse, and people from many different cultures lived and worked together. Today African Americans, Mexican Americans, and Native Americans lived side by side. People originally from places like Europe, Asia, and the Middle East made the community work.

"Our mural should celebrate all the people—young and old—who make a contribution," said Renata.

"Our town's history and diverse culture should shine through in the scenes on the mural," said Tanya.

Ms. Sanchez found a professional artist, and he volunteered to work with the students. Together they sketched a design for their mural, worked out a plan for funding, mailed it to city hall, and waited.

It took two weeks while everyone hoped nervously for approval. Finally, Mayor Pena and the town council approved the design. They also offered a wall of the community center as a location. The mural was really going to happen!

That same day the class divided the project. Four teams would each paint a panel. Each team would work on a different afternoon or Saturday.

Renata's fingers were itching to start on all the ideas in her mind. She could not wait to begin painting. Her team would make the first panel, showing the history of their community. That night she got out her palette and began to experiment with colors for wagons, pueblos, and maize. She painted small versions of the panel and then added people and details, such as the expressions on their faces. Tomorrow could not come soon enough!

The next afternoon her team began sketching on the wall of the community center. No one dawdled, and no one was bored.

The team drew squares on the wall to match the squares on their sketch. The details in a square would be reproduced, only larger, on the mural. Renata helped direct the work. A rough outline began to take shape.

As the mural grew, curious people stopped to watch.

"That's my pueblo!" cried one man.

"My great-grandmother traveled here in a wagon like that," a woman stated proudly.

The local newspaper sent a reporter, who wrote an article about the mural. After this publicity a stream of people began to show up, wanting to know what they could do to help.

Within a week, talk of the mural had spread all over town. Neighbors discussed what each panel showed about their community. You could hear people in the coffee shops telling stories about what the town must have been like a hundred years ago. People started to think about who they were and where they had come from, and what the town might be like fifty years from now! They wondered what people and events would appear next on the mural.

The parents of Renata's classmates came with snacks and drinks for the artists. Then they sat together and talked as the work progressed.

Weeks passed quickly. Ms. Sanchez's students labored like a hive of busy bees. They completed the shapes and added special details. They brushed, splashed, and smoothed colorful paints. The mural was like a puzzle with all of the pieces coming together.

"The mural will be unveiled November 18," Ms. Sanchez announced to a curious reporter.

Renata thought to herself, *Will we finish in time? And, will the mural be good enough?*

While the students continued their work, people in the community were planning a block party with food and music to represent each culture shown in the mural. Everyone was proud of the students and of their community.

As she put the finishing touches on a wagon train, Renata became more and more excited! She wondered how the mural would look when all the panels were complete. No one had seen the whole thing at once because each team covered their work when they finished a session. She hoped that all of the teams' pieces would hold together and not clash.

Finally there was only one more night to wait. The big day was tomorrow. As her mother and grandmother rolled fresh tamales for the block party, Renata dreamed of the unveiling.

November 18 was a clear, cool Saturday. The sun shone brightly down on the street. The block was packed with smiling, chatting people eagerly awaiting the unveiling of the mural that was like a huge unopened present. Renata thought, *We did it! We brought people together! I hope they like the paintings!*

Ms. Sanchez welcomed everyone and explained the project. Then Mayor Peña congratulated the students. Excitement mounted as she and Ms. Sanchez climbed up ladders. A large plastic sheet covered the mural. It flapped in the breeze. With a flourish, they pulled away the cover.

For a minute there was silence. Renata felt a lump in her throat, and her eyes were stinging. She was not sad, though—she felt wonderful!

The mural was beautiful, and it was powerful. It wove the past, the present, and the future together and was full of every kind of life in the community. Taking it in made her feel both solemn and joyful at the same time.

The townspeople must have agreed with Renata. A huge cheer went up from hundreds of people. The students of Ms. Sanchez's sixth-grade class took a bow, celebrating their triumph. Then the music and feasting began.

Vocabulary

heritage (her´ i tij) (page 4) *n.* Something handed down from earlier generations or from the past; tradition.

diverse (di vûrs´) (page 7) *adj.* Not all the same; varied.

palette (pal´ it) (page 9) *n.* A thin, oval board on which artists place and mix their paints.

dawdled (dôd´ əld) (page 9) *v.* Past tense of **dawdle:** To move idly.

publicity (pu blis´ i tē) (page 10) *n.* Information given out to bring a person or thing to the attention of the public.

mounted (mount´ əd) (page 14) *v.* Past tense of **mount:** To rise or increase.

solemn (sol´ əm) (page 15) *adj.* Very serious.

triumph (trī´ umf) (page 15) *n.* A great success.

Comprehension Focus: Making Inferences

1. What inferences can you make about the mayor based on her actions in the story?

2. What inferences can you make about the people in the community who are excited to see the mural?